Chip had a box.

1

He put sand in it.

"Pat it flat," he said.

Kipper had a box.

He put sand in it.

Biff had a bucket.

She put sand in it.

Biff put the bucket on top.

"Good," she said.

It was a sandcastle.

It was a good sandcastle.

It was the best sandcastle.